An Int
to Navigation

by Melanie Bartlett FRIN

© Melanie Bartlett 2010
First Published 2010
Reprinted February 2013, August 2014,
November 2015, November 2016,
March 2018, April 2019, January 2020,
January 2021, March 2022
The Royal Yachting Association
RYA House, Ensign Way, Hamble,
Southampton SO31 4YA
Tel: 02380 604 100
Web: www.rya.org.uk
Follow us on Twitter @RYAPublications or
on YouTube

We welcome feedback on our
publications at publications@rya.org.uk

You can check for content updates for RYA
publications at www.rya.org.uk/go/
bookschangelog

ISBN: 978-1906-435-080
RYA Order Code: G77

Cover Design: Tony Collins
Typesetting and Design: Kevin Slater
Proofreading and indexing: Alan Thatcher
Photographic credit: Paul Wyeth
Printed in China through World Print

Sustainable
Forests

Foreword

To the untrained eye, navigation can appear a devilishly complicated business, but the fact is that sailors from every walk of life have been using the same basic principles for centuries and you certainly don't need to be a rocket scientist to navigate a coastal passage safely and competently.

Navigation is a vital skill to have when you are afloat. Yet, in an age of GPS, it is all too tempting to rely on modern technology to find your way. Without a firm grasp of the basics, however, you will never be able to navigate with the confidence and assurance that true knowledge gives you.

Melanie Bartlett is the ideal author to introduce you to the basics. Hugely experienced as an RYA Yachtmaster Instructor, she also presents the subject in an informal and user friendly style which ensures that the novice is not intimidated.

This book will leave you wanting to learn more, and this is important, as there are few greater pleasures afloat than safely navigating your boat to a safe haven, using skills that are centuries old.

James Stevens FRIN

TO LEARN TO NAVIGATE YOU WILL NEED: Breton Plotter (or similar); dividers; soft pencil; soft eraser; pencil sharpener; practice charts; practice navigation tables; navigation exercises.

TO PRACTICE NAVIGATION AT SEA YOU WILL ALSO NEED: appropriate charts; a yachtsmen's almanac; a steering compass; a hand bearing compass; a log; an echo sounder; a GPS receiver.

Contents

Charts used in this book are RYA Training Charts and are not to be used for navigation.

Chapter 1: **Introduction**

We are all navigators.

But on land our "navigation" is often limited to following a ribbon of tarmac, while being spoon-fed – sometimes force-fed – with instructions and information: "Stop"; "Slow down", or "London 33 miles".

At sea, navigators are more like hunters, picking up pieces of information, looking for clues, and making their own decisions.

It's not necessarily difficult, and it certainly shouldn't be haphazard, but it is far more interesting than navigating on land.

Marine maps

Maps – called "charts" at sea – are absolutely fundamental. They can be printed on paper or stored and displayed on an electronic chart plotter rather like an in-car navigator.

The extract (Chart 1) is adapted from an RYA Practice Chart and uses British Admiralty colours and symbols. Charts from other publishers may use different colours, but they share many of the same features:

■ The coastline.

■ Depth information.

■ Symbols representing hazards and landmarks.

■ A grid of latitude and longitude.

The coastline

The most obvious feature of this chart is that some areas are yellow, while others are white, blue, or green.

▥ Land is yellow.

▥ Water in blue or white.

▥ Areas which are sometimes above water and sometimes below it, are green.

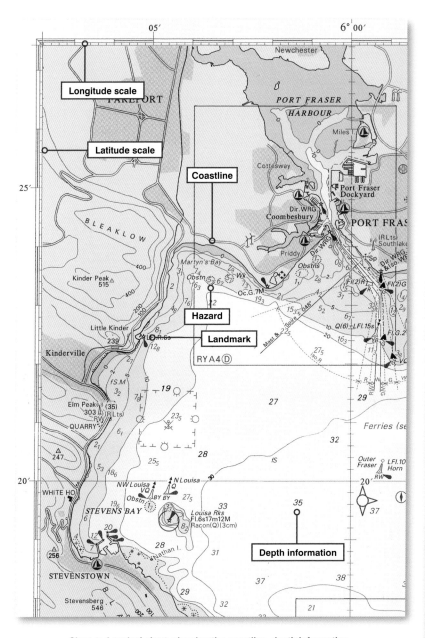

Chart 1: A typical chart, showing the coastline, depth information,
landmarks, hazards, and a grid of latitude and longitude

Depth information

There are two distinct ways of representing heights and depths on a chart.

Spot depths show the depth at particular spots. They are dotted around all over the chart (Fig 1).

Contours are usually defined as "lines that join points of equal height or depth", but it's more useful to think of them as being lines that divide shallow water from deep (Fig 2).

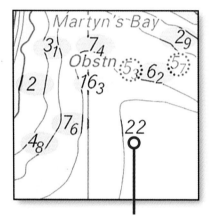

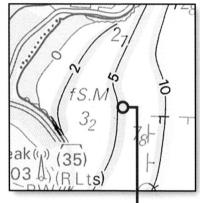

Fig 1: Spot depths show the depth at
particular spots

Fig 2: Contours are lines that divide
shallow water from deep

To make this distinction particularly clear, shallow areas are coloured blue while deep areas are coloured white – often with pale blue being used for intermediate depths.

In the top right-hand corner of Chart 1 on page 5, we can see from the green area that most of Port Fraser harbour is sometimes above water and sometimes below it, and that there is an area of shallow water (represented by the blue tint) around the approaches. But the thin strip of paler blue shows that there is a deeper channel, zig-zagging in from the bottom right hand corner of the extract, towards the entrance, then branching out inside the harbour.

Symbols and abbreviations

The chart extract below is drawn to a scale of 1:100,000. That means that every centimetre on the chart represents 100,000 centimetres (one kilometre) in the real world.

Fig 3: A star-shaped symbol represents a lighthouse

Fig 4: Buoys are represented by pictures of the buoys themselves

Some important features are far too small to show up at this scale. A lighthouse, for instance (Fig 3), might be 50 metres high, but only 15 metres in diameter, so on a 1:100,000 chart it would be represented by a spot barely one eighth of a millimetre in diameter.

To overcome this problem, symbols are used to represent important features.

A star-shaped symbol represents a lighthouse, with a white spot in the centre of the star showing its exact position, and a string of letters and numbers alongside it giving more information.

In this example, Fl.6s17m12M means that it shows a white light, flashing once every six seconds at an elevation of 17 metres and with a nominal range of 12 miles.

Just above Louisa Rocks lighthouse are two buoys, indicated by line drawings that represent the shapes of the buoys themselves (Fig 4). Like the lighthouse, their exact positions are marked by a small circle in the base of each buoy, while abbreviations around them provide additional information:

VQ BY, for instance, tells us that NW Louisa is black and yellow, and that it shows a very quick flashing light.

There are so many chart symbols that no-one can learn them all at once: it is better to become familiar with the most important ones (buoys, lighthouses, and churches; rocks, wrecks, and prohibited areas) and to be ready to look up any others as you come across them (Fig 1).

The definitive guide to UK Admiralty chart symbols is a slim booklet known as Chart 5011, available from the RYA webshop, and extracts from it are on the back of some Admiralty charts and in publications such as the Reeds Nautical Almanac.

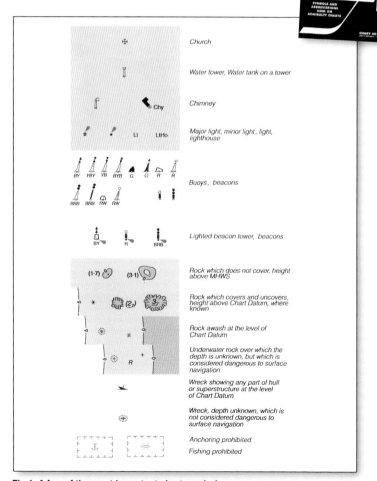

Fig 1: A few of the most important chart symbols

An Introduction to Navigation

Latitude and Longitude

Land maps usually have a grid of lines to help locate particular features. Charts have a similar grid, except that instead of being purely arbitrary, like the grid in a road atlas, the grid on a chart refers to the international grid of Latitude and Longitude, based on natural reference points (Fig 2).

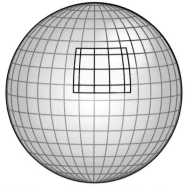

Fig 2: The world-wide grid of lat and long is based on natural reference points

The most important of these natural references are the north and south poles and the Equator.

A good working definition of **Latitude** is:

▨ The Latitude of a place is its distance from the Equator, expressed as an angle (Fig 3), so

▨ The Latitude of a place tells us how far north or south it is.

▨ Lines that join places of equal latitude run parallel to the Equator. On a chart, they appear as horizontal lines.

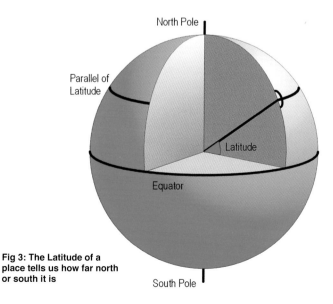

Fig 3: The Latitude of a place tells us how far north or south it is

The corresponding vertical lines are called meridians. On a global scale, meridians run from pole to pole, dividing the world into segments as though it were a giant orange.

By international agreement, the meridian that passes through Greenwich, in south-east London, is taken as the "Prime Meridian".

The Longitude of a place is the angle between the Prime Meridian and the meridian of the place measured around the Equator in degrees at the centre of the Earth (Fig 1), so

The Longitude of a place tells us how far east or west it is.

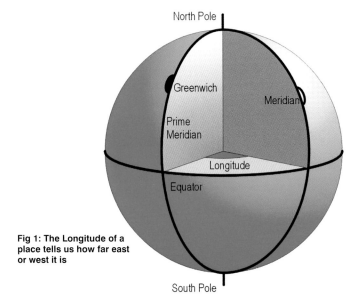

Fig 1: The Longitude of a place tells us how far east or west it is

Combining Latitude and Longitude enables us to specify particular positions: Falmouth, for instance, is at 50°N 005°W.

To specify positions more accurately, each degree is subdivided into sixtieths, called minutes, and each minute is further subdivided into tenths, hundredths, or thousandths.

The chart opposite shows that the position of Louisa Rocks lighthouse is 46° 19'.3 N 006° 04'.6 W. Notice that latitude is given first and that their directions (North or South and East or West) are always included.

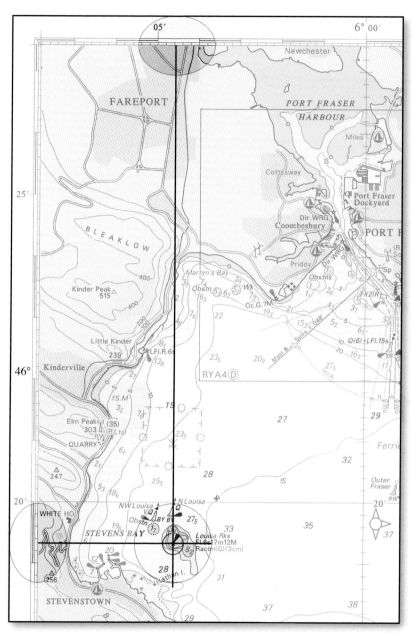

The chart shows that the position of Louisa Rocks lighthouse
is 46° 19'.3 N 006° 04'.6 W

An Introduction to Navigation   11

Chapter 2: **Direction and Distance**

Distance

Distance, at sea, is usually measured in sea miles or nautical miles.

- A sea mile is defined as a minute of latitude measured at the Earth's surface.

- A nautical mile is 1852 metres. It's so close to the length of a sea mile that for most practical purposes, the two units can be treated as being the same.

- Speed is measured in knots. A knot is one nautical mile per hour.

Measuring distance in the real world

To measure the distance we have travelled, we use an instrument known as a log (Fig 1).

The commonest type uses a small paddlewheel that sticks out from the bottom of the boat. As the boat moves through the water, the paddlewheel spins, and an electronic sensor counts the revolutions.

Fig 1: A typical log, measuring speed and distance through the water

Measuring distance on a chart

The fact that a sea mile is a minute of Latitude means that the scale of Latitude on the side of a chart serves as a scale of distance.

A slight snag is that you seldom want to measure distances in a north-south direction, close to the edge of the chart! So we need some way to transfer distances measured up or down the latitude scale to other directions and other parts of the chart.

The tool for the job is known as a pair of dividers (Fig 2).

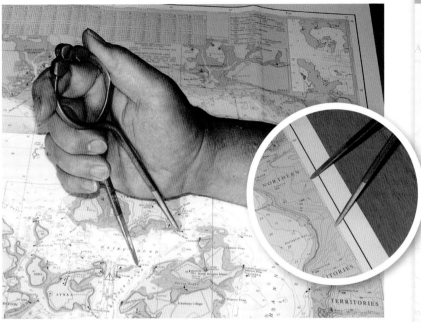

Fig 2: Dividers are used to measure distances on the chart

There are two kinds.

Straight dividers have straight legs, which can
be opened or closed by pushing and pulling the points

Single-handed dividers (Fig 3) can be opened
with one hand, simply by squeezing
the bulging "bow" at the top
of the legs, or closed
with the same
hand by squeezing
the lower part of the legs together.

**Fig 3: Single-handed
dividers**

Direction

■ The meridians run from north to south (or vice versa).

■ The parallels cross the meridians at right angles, from west to east (or east to west).

■ These four directions are called cardinal points.

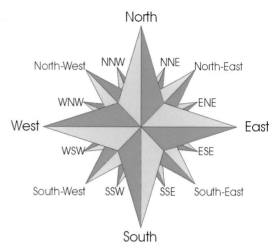

Fig 1: Compass points are still used to indicate approximate directions

Directions in between the cardinal points can be given names too. North east, for instance, is half-way between north and east (Fig 1).

For most navigational purposes however we need the greater precision that is provided by three figure notation, in which directions are referred to as angles, measured in degrees, counting clockwise from north (Fig 2).

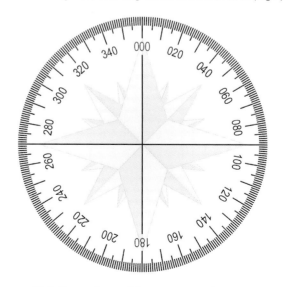

Fig 2: For greater precision, we now use degrees

Measuring direction in the real world

Any sea-going boat needs at least one compass. In practice, most carry at least two or three.

■ One is fixed to the structure of the boat to show the direction she is pointing, so it is called the steering compass.

■ Another is a smaller, hand-held version used for measuring bearings (the direction between you and some other object), so it is called a hand bearing compass.

■ Both types use small magnets clipped to the bottom of a circular compass card to sense the direction of the Earth's magnetic field.

■ A third type of compass is becoming increasingly common. It uses a cluster of electronic components called flux gates to measure the direction of the Earth's magnetic field, and sends information about the boat's heading to other electronic devices such as chart plotters or radars.

Using a steering compass

Most steering compasses consist of a circular compass card, marked in degrees, mounted inside a transparent bowl (Fig 3). Also inside the bowl, is a vertical line – the lubber line – representing the bow of the boat.

Steering by compass takes practice, but in theory it is simply a matter of keeping the lubber line lined up with the direction you want to go.

Fig 3: A steering compass

Lubber line

Using a hand bearing compass

There are two main types of hand bearing compass.

One is rather like a small steering compass, mounted on a handle (Fig 1). To use, hold the compass at arm's length, towards the object whose bearing you are trying to measure. Look across the compass, trying to get both lubber lines and the distant landmark lined up with each other. In the photograph, the bearing of the chimney is 160°.

Fig 1: A hand bearing compass

In calm conditions, you may be able to read off the bearing directly from the edge of the card (remembering that the edge scale reads backwards!). When the going gets more lively, you will probably have to take a mental average of several readings as the card swings.

The other type is much smaller, and is designed to be held up close to the eye. A prism built into the top of the compass allows you to see the numbers on the front of the compass card – magnified and in focus – while you look across the compass to more distant objects beyond. Most compasses of this type have a lubber line visible through the prism, but it's not really necessary: you read off the compass scale immediately below the target object. In the photograph, the bearing of the church is 163° (Fig 2).

Like the arm's length compass, this type is easy to use in calm conditions, but as the boat starts jumping about you are likely to find yourself having to take a mental average from a swinging card.

Fig 2: Using a prismatic compass to take a bearing

Compass errors

All magnetic compasses are prone to two distinct errors, variation and deviation.

1. VARIATION is caused by the fact that the Earth's magnetic field is not perfectly lined up with its axis of spin. As the name suggests, variation varies from place to place and from year to year. (Fig 3)

The amount of variation, along with the date and the rate at which it is changing, is printed on the chart. There is nothing we can do to reduce it: we can only be aware of it, and allow for it arithmetically.

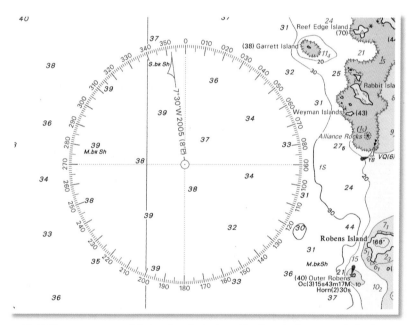

Fig 3: Compass roses, printed on the chart, show directions in degrees and give the difference between true and magnetic North

2. Deviation is caused by magnetic materials on board the boat making the compass deviate. The fact that it is caused by objects within the boat itself means that its effect on the compass may change quite significantly as the boat alters course, so a professional compass adjuster can be employed to produce a deviation card showing the deviation on different headings (Fig 1).

DEVIATION CARD

Compass... *LOWER*

Vessel... *FAIRLINE 55·01*

Date... *18th JUNE 2008*

Position... *IPSWICH*

Compass Adjuster... *Peter Garrod*

MCA Cert No... *170C*

SEATH INSTRUMENTS (1992) LTD
Unit 30 Colville Road Works,
Colville Road, Lowestoft, Suffolk NR33 9QS
Tel: 01502 573811 Fax: 0502 514173
www.Seath-Haztec.com
Marine Instruments & Manufacturers of Haztec Gas Detectors

HEAD	DEV.	HEAD	DEV.
000	0	180	0
022	2E	202	0
045	2E	225	0
067	2E	247	2W
090	0	270	2W
112	0	292	2W
135	0	315	0
157	0	337	0

**Fig 1: A deviation card, produced by a compass adjuster,
shows the error of a particular compass**

In this instance, we can see that the deviation was 0 when the boat was heading North (000), increasing to 2°E when the boat was heading North east (045), reducing to zero again when it was heading East (090).

A couple of degrees of deviation is hardly enough to worry about, but a carelessly-placed radio or anything containing a magnet or ferrous metal can easily deviate a compass by 20 or 30 degrees, making it almost completely useless. So even the most casual navigator really needs to be aware of deviation, and take care to keep magnets and magnetic objects as far from the compass as possible.

Correcting for compass errors

The fact that there are two kinds of compass error means that we have to get used to dealing with three kinds of north.

1. Compass North is the direction shown by a compass

Deviation separates it from...

2. Magnetic North, which is the direction of North that would be shown by a magnetic compass if there were no deviation.

Variation separates it from...

3. True North, which is the direction of a meridian towards the North Pole

Suppose, for instance, that we know that the deviation of our steering compass is 2 degrees East.

This means that the North mark on the card has been pulled a couple of degrees to the east – so North (Compass) is really 002°(Magnetic).

In other words, to convert from Compass to Magnetic we have to add easterly errors.

The same rule applies when we need to convert from Magnetic to True: if the variation were 5°E, we would have to add 5° – so 002° (Magnetic) would become 007° (True).

The rule is that when converting from **Compass** to **True**, you **Add Easterly** errors.

Generations of navigators have used the word CadeT to remember this, because to get from the C to T you have to Ad (add) E (Fig 2).

Fig 2: The CadeT rule is a handy reminder of how to correct for compass errors

So long as you can remember that, it is pretty obvious that:

to get from **Compass** to **True**, you **Subtract Westerly** errors,

to get from **True** to **Compass**, you **Add Westerly** errors, and

to get from **True** to **Compass**, you **Subtract Easterly** errors

Checking for deviation

Checking for deviation is known as swinging the compass. There are several possible methods, but the most suitable for the majority of small boats is known as a swing by distant objects.

The process is simple:-

■ Take the boat to a known position (ideally one where there is a fixed mark such as a pile or beacon surrounded by navigable water) and aim the bows at each of several distant landmarks in turn, noting the compass bearing (direction) of each landmark as you do so.

■ Then, on the chart, measure the true bearing of each landmark from your known position.

■ Convert the true bearings to magnetic bearings, by adding westerly variation (or subtracting easterly variation).

■ Compare the magnetic bearing of each landmark with the compass bearing you measured with your own compass. The difference between them is the compass error.

■ If the compass bearing is greater than the magnetic bearing, label the error **west**.

■ If the compass bearing is less than the magnetic bearing, label the error **east**.

Fig 1: A "swing by distant objects" simply involves taking the boat to a known position and aiming at each of several distant landmarks in turn

Measuring direction on a chart

As well as the grid of meridians and parallels, most charts include a number of compass roses consisting of a circular scale of degrees showing directions relative to True north (see chart below). Some, generally on older charts, have an inner circle, showing directions relative to Magnetic north.

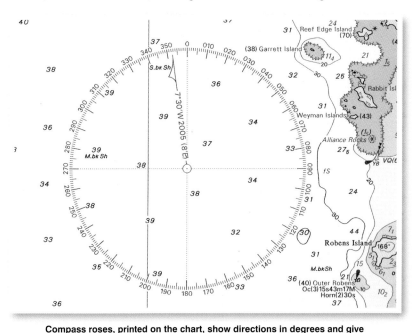

Compass roses, printed on the chart, show directions in degrees and give the difference between true and magnetic North

As when measuring distance, the slight snag with this is that you almost never want to measure directions to or from the centre of a compass rose! All sorts of gadgets have been invented to overcome the problem, but the most popular is the Breton Plotter (Fig 2).

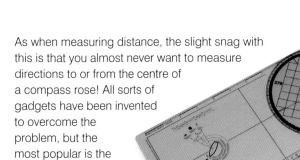

Fig 2: Breton Plotter

An Introduction to Navigation

Using a Breton Plotter

A Breton Plotter – and its many copies – consists of a transparent rectangular base, with a rotating circular protractor mounted at the centre.

■ **To measure the direction of a line** on the chart, place the plotter on the chart with one of its long edges lined up with the line. Then rotate the protractor so that the lines marked on it are parallel to the meridians and parallels on the chart, with the north mark pointing north (Fig 1).

Fig 1: Using a Breton Plotter to measure the direction of a line on a chart

Read off the direction of the line by looking at where the centreline of the base crosses the edge of the protractor.

In Fig 1, the direction of the line on the chart is 073°.

■ **To draw a line in a particular direction** is almost exactly the reverse:

Turn the protractor until the required direction is lined up with the centreline of the base. Then place the plotter on the chart, and adjust its position until the grid marked on the protractor is lined up with the grid on the chart.

Finally, using a soft pencil draw a line along the long edge of the plotter.

An Introduction to Navigation

Measuring depth

Old-fashioned methods for measuring water depth involved feeling for the bottom with sticks or weights on strings, but this has been replaced by electronic echo sounders and fish finders.

The main difference between the two is that a fish finder (Fig 2) produces a graphical representation of the changing depth, whereas an echo sounder (Fig 3) gives a digital read-out.

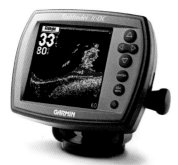

Fig 2: A fish finder works on the same principle as an echo sounder, but gives a graphic indication of changing depths

Fig 3: An echo sounder gives a digital indication of the depth of water

Different kinds of direction

Direction is so important in navigation that we have several different words for it, each one referring to a different kind of direction: (Fig 4)

- **Bearing** – the direction of one object from another.
- **Course** – the direction the vessel is being steered.
- **Heading** – the direction the vessel happens to be pointing at any given moment.
- **Track angle** – the direction the vessel is actually moving: it is often abbreviated to Track, and can also be known as Ground Track, Course Made Good, or Course over Ground.
- **Water Track** – the direction the vessel is moving through the water, and sometimes called the Wake Course.

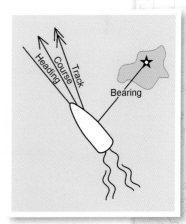

Fig 4: As navigators, we are concerned with several different kinds of "direction"

Chapter 3: **GPS**

Until the last few years of the twentieth century, most of the work of a small-boat navigator was concerned with finding out where they were.

But back in 1978, the American Department of Defence launched the first satellite of a new Global Positioning System (GPS) that has revolutionised the way we find our way around. Hand-held GPS receivers (Fig 1) can tell us our position, anywhere in the world, at any time and in any weather, to within a few metres. More sophisticated versions keep track of our progress on moving map displays in cars (SatNav), while their marine counterparts – chart plotters – do the same job at sea. (Fig 2)

Fig 1: Hand-held GPS receivers can tell us our position, anywhere in the world

Fig 2: A chart plotter shows the boat's position on a moving electronic map

Basic operation

Some features and functions are standard in all basic GPS receivers, but their controls and operating procedures vary so much that there is no substitute for reading the manufacturer's instruction manual for your particular model.

Switching on

When you switch on a GPS receiver for the first time, or after it has been moved a long distance while switched off, it may take several minutes to calculate its position.

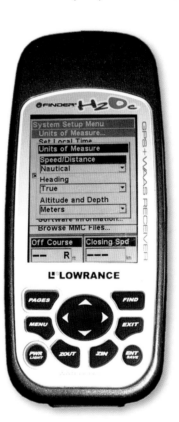

This delay is a good opportunity to get into the setup functions to customise it to your individual preferences. Some features are largely cosmetic, such as whether it beeps when you press a key and whether it displays dates in British or American format, but others are more important. (Fig 3)

In particular it is worth making certain that:

■ Units are set to nautical (nautical miles and knots)

■ Direction is set to True and measured in degrees

■ **Position** is displayed as latitude and longitude, in degrees, minutes, and decimals

■ **Horizontal Datum** is set to match the datum specified on the title panel of the chart you are using – usually "WGS 84"

Fig 3: When a GPS set is first switched on, it may take some time to find itself. This is a good time to make sure that it is set up to suit marine use – displaying nautical miles and latitude and longitude rather than kilometres and grid references

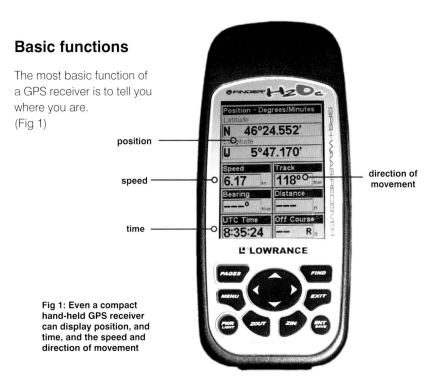

Basic functions

The most basic function of a GPS receiver is to tell you where you are.
(Fig 1)

position

speed

time

direction of movement

Fig 1: Even a compact hand-held GPS receiver can display position, and time, and the speed and direction of movement

As a by-product of the way it calculates position, it can tell the time – more accurately than any conventional clock. And by comparing the way your position changes over a period of time, it can calculate the direction and speed of your movement. Different manufacturers use different terminology:

■ **Direction** may be called   course (CRS)

                                         track (TRK)

    or   course over ground (CoG)

■ **Speed** may be called   speed (SPD)

                                         velocity (VEL)

    or   speed over ground (S0G)

It is worth remembering that a GPS set is not a compass, so it cannot show the direction your boat is pointing – only the direction it is moving. Nor can it measure your speed through the water – it shows the speed at which you are moving over the ground.

Waypoints

As well as basic functions, all GPS sets are also able to store a number of fixed positions called waypoints.

The original idea was that a route between two places could be drawn on a chart as a series of straight lines from one waypoint to the next.

Go To

The simplest route of all is a straight line from where you are to where you want to go. Many GPS sets have a dedicated Go To function that allows a single waypoint to be set as a destination, without going through the more complex process of setting up a route (Fig 2).

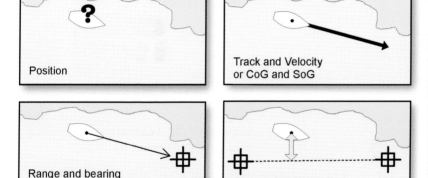

Fig 2: Once you have told it where you want to go, the navigation computer within the GPS can calculate a lot more useful information

As soon as you have told your GPS that you want to go to a particular waypoint, it is able to supply new information, comparing your changing position with that of the fixed waypoint. The two most obvious pieces of information are the direction and distance to the waypoint, known as its range (distance) and bearing (direction).

Another very useful piece of information is how far you have strayed from the straight line between waypoints. This is usually known as your cross track error, and is usually abbreviated to XTE.

Plotting GPS positions

It's no use knowing where you are unless you can relate it to the world around you. To do this, the position indicated by a GPS set has to be plotted on a chart.

Latitude and Longitude

The most obvious way is to use the latitude and longitude shown on the position display. Suppose, for instance, that the GPS says we are at 46° 23.'2N 005° 52.'4W.

The first step is to look on the chart, to find a nearby meridian and parallel

1. Then use the latitude scale on the side of the chart to set the dividers to the distance between the parallel we have chosen (in this case 46° 20'N) and the latitude we need to plot (46° 23.'2N).

2. Transfer the dividers to the nearest meridian, and make a mark at 46° 23.'2N.

3. Draw an east-west line through the mark.

4. Use the longitude scale on the top or bottom of the chart to set the dividers to the distance between the meridian we have chosen (005° 50'W) and the longitude we need to plot (005° 52.'4W).

5. Transfer the dividers to the east-west pencil line, to make a mark at 005° 52.'4W.

6. Standard practice is to mark the position with a circle and the time.

It's not essential to do things in this order, it may be easier to use parallel rulers or a plotter to draw a meridian straight downwards from 005° 52.'4W, rather than using dividers.

No matter how you do it, plotting a latitude and longitude like this can easily take a few minutes which may cause problems if travelling at speed.

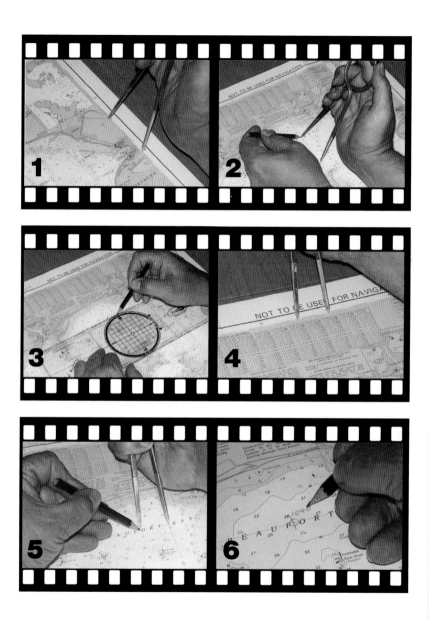

Quick plotting by range and bearing

As soon as we have a waypoint saved in the GPS set's memory, the range and bearing function gives us an alternative way of plotting our position.

In this example (see chart below), we might be heading for Namley Harbour, with the red beacon off Namley Bar as our Go To waypoint, and the GPS showing its range and bearing as 3.9 miles, 068°.

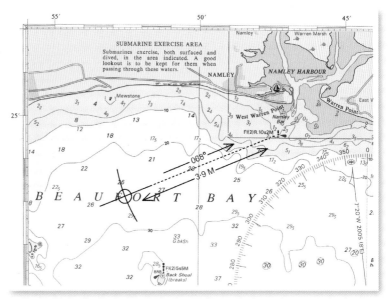

A position plotted by range and bearing may not be very precise, but it is quick and simple

If the beacon is on a bearing of 068° from us, then our position on the chart must be somewhere along a line drawn in a 068° direction, passing through the beacon.

But the GPS is also telling us that the beacon is 3.9 miles away. So we can find our actual position simply by measuring 3.9 miles from the beacon, along the line that we've just drawn.

A position plotted by range and bearing may not be quite as precise as one that is based on latitude and longitude, but it has the advantage of being plotted much more quickly and with less chance of making a mistake.

Variations on plotting by range and bearing

There is no reason why the range and bearing technique has to use the waypoint you are aiming for. The most accurate result will always be achieved by using a near waypoint rather than a distant one, so at the start of a passage it is better to refer back to the waypoint you have just left, rather than to the one that is ahead but further away.

Another possibility is to use a purely arbitrary waypoint, such as the centre of one of the compass roses printed on the chart. The beauty of this is that it makes it very easy to plot the bearing accurately: you don't even need a Breton Plotter — any straight edge will do, because it can be lined up directly on the compass rose itself.

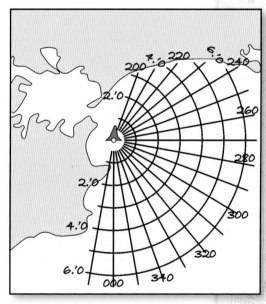

A third variation is to draw your own compass rose around a waypoint that you are likely to use regularly, such as the entrance to your home port, and add range rings – concentric circles, drawn at regular intervals – to produce a pattern rather like a spider's web (Fig 1). It takes time to construct the spider's web, but it is particularly useful for very small or very fast boats, because it means that a position can be plotted quickly when you are under way, without any chartwork instruments whatsoever.

Fig 1: A pre-drawn "spider's web" makes plotting range and bearing even quicker and easier

Quick plotting by range and cross track error

One of the problems associated with using a bearing (direction) is that the effect of any error in the bearing is magnified at long ranges.

Where the beacon was 3.9 miles away, a couple of degrees of error in plotting the direction of the line would have produced a position error of about 200 metres. If we had been using a lighthouse 20 miles away, the same plotting error would have increased the positioning error to 1000 metres.

One way to deal with this is to use the GPS set's cross track error (XTE) function rather than the bearing to waypoint (Chart 1).

Suppose, for instance that we have now left Namley, and are heading for Rawmarsh, and that the GPS is showing that we are five miles from our waypoint at Rawmarsh.

It is easy to measure back from the waypoint along the line showing the planned route, and to make a mark, five miles from the waypoint (Chart 1).

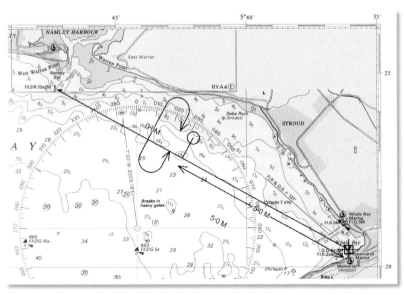

Chart 1: Range and XTE are a good way of monitoring position while on passage

An Introduction to Navigation

If, at the same time, the cross track error display shows that we are 0.6 miles to port of track, we can plot our actual position by measuring 0.6 miles from the five-mile mark, off to the port side of the planned track.

With a little more effort in the planning stage, this technique can be made even easier, by drawing reference lines (see Chart 2 below), but a half a mile or a mile on each side of the intended track and marking of the distance to go at regular intervals.

This pre-drawn "ladder" plot has a lot in common with the "spider's web": it is particularly useful for boats with limited navigation facilities, or lively motion, or for single-handers, and its drawback is that some accuracy has to be sacrificed in favour of speed and simplicity. But so long as the cross track error is relatively small compared with the distance to the waypoint, the positioning error is unlikely to be significant (Chart 2).

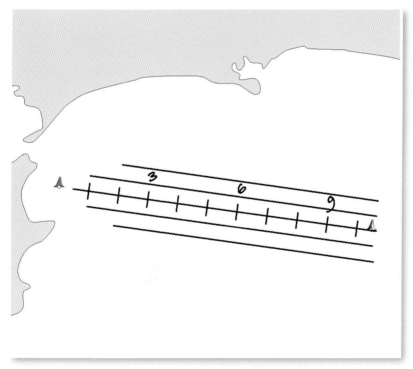

Chart 2: A pre-drawn "ladder" simplifies plotting while under way

Chapter 4: **Visual fixing**

Traditional navigation involves three different kinds of position:

▓ Dead reckoning.

▓ Estimated position.

▓ Fixed position.

A dead reckoning position or **DR** is based purely on the course steered and the distance travelled.

It sounds reasonable enough, until you bear in mind that boats are easily pushed sideways by the wind, and in any direction by the movement of the water on which they float.

An estimated position or **EP** is considerably better, because it allows for the effect of wind and tide.

Best of all is a fixed position or **fix**, in which the boat's position has been confirmed by comparing it with some outside reference point such as a GPS satellite or a lighthouse.

The simplest fix of all

One of the best and simplest fixes is sometimes called a single point fix because it involves no more than passing close to a fixed and identifiable object. (see chart opposite)

It's particularly useful at the start and end of a passage, when you are likely to be passing very close to the end of a harbour wall or breakwater, or a mark such as a buoy or beacon.

The key things to look for are:

1. It must be possible to pass so close to the object that we can safely ignore or estimate the distance between its position and ours.

2. It must be clearly shown on the chart.

3. It must be positively identified in the real world.

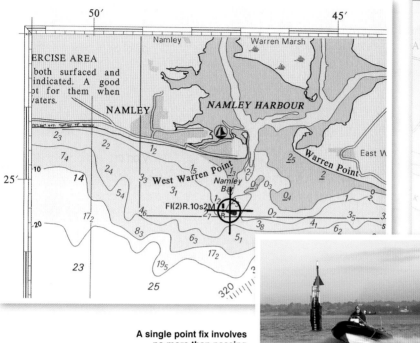

Position line fixes

A single point fix is simple, but not very convenient. For a position fix – on demand – we need a more sophisticated technique.

The principle is very much the same as plotting a GPS position by range and bearing.

In the previous chapter, for instance, we said:-

"If the beacon is on a bearing of 068° from us, then our position on the chart must be somewhere along a line drawn in a 068° direction, passing through the beacon."

In that particular case, the bearing to the beacon was supplied by the GPS, but it could equally well have been measured with a hand bearing compass. That line is known as a position line – because our position must be somewhere along it.

Suppose, for instance, that we can see Holm Point lighthouse on a bearing of about 302°(M) (see chart opposite).

That bearing was taken with a magnetic hand bearing compass, so we first need to convert it from Magnetic to True. The nearby Compass Rose says that Variation was 7°20'W in 2005, and that it is changing 8'E every year, so by now the variation must be a bit less than 7°. (There is no point messing about with fractions of a degree, because a hand bearing compass simply isn't that accurate!)

The CADET rule (from page 19) tells us that westerly variation has to be subtracted, so the True bearing of the lighthouse is 302°(M) - 7° = 295°(T).

One position line by itself doesn't tell us very much, but there is another lighthouse on Mutton Head, on a bearing of 233°(M). Doing the same conversion: 233°(M) - 7° = 226°(T).

In theory, the one place that we can possibly be on both position lines at once is where they cross.

In practice, it is always possible to misread the compass, or to wrongly identify a landmark, and it is almost inevitable that the boat will have moved in the time it takes to take the fix. So it is best to take and plot the bearing of a third object. Each of the three position lines then serves as a cross-check on the other two, because they should all cross at a single point. In practice, they almost never do: instead, they form a triangle called a cocked hat.

The size of the cocked hat gives a good idea of the reliability of the fix: a small, neat cocked hat is generally a sign of a reliable fix, whereas a big floppy one suggests that something has gone wrong.

Six rules are the key to getting a tidy cocked hat:
1. Make sure your landmarks can be positively identified on the chart and in the real world.
2. Choose objects that are well spread around the horizon.
3. Choose near objects rather than distant ones.
4. Take bearings which are changing slowly first and those that are changing quickly last.
5. Take bearings of distant objects as accurately as possible.
6. Take bearings of near objects as quickly as possible.

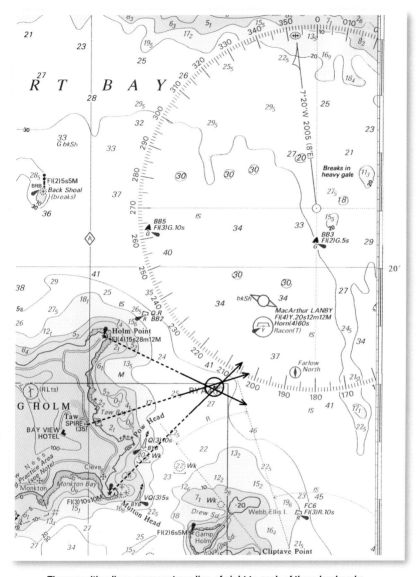

Three position lines represent our line of sight to each of three landmarks.
There is only one place where we can be on all three lines at once!

Other position lines

A position line doesn't have to be a bearing. It doesn't even have to be straight.

Transits

Perhaps the most useful of the alternative position lines is a transit. A transit occurs whenever two objects appear to be in line with each other, such as the church and water tower in the photograph (Fig 1).

**Fig 1: At the moment the water tower disappeared behind the church,
they were in transit with each other**

So long as both objects are identifiable on the chart, plotting a transit as a position line is a simple matter of drawing a straight line on the chart that passes through both objects.

A transit is almost an ideal position line, because it is quick and easy to take and to plot and is not affected by variation or deviation. The only snag with transits is that they aren't available on demand: you have to plot a transit when it arises, not when you want it!

Contours

Contours can also serve as position lines.

Imagine, for the moment, that you are in an area where there is no tide, and that your echo sounder shows that you are in 10m of water. You must be somewhere on a 10m contour, so the contour itself is a position line – albeit a wiggly one!

In real life, things are seldom quite so simple.

For one thing, you usually have to allow for the effect of the tide – see Chapter 5 – which almost always means that the actual depth of water is slightly more than the depth shown on the chart. For another, you are seldom likely to look at the echo sounder at the precise moment that you cross a convenient contour line. And finally, as contour lines can never cross each other, you can only ever get one contour position line at a time. To get a fix, you will have to combine the contour line with something else – such as a visual bearing.

In practice, it pays to plan a depth-based position line in advance, calculating the height of tide and working out what the echo sounder should read as you cross a convenient contour. Then, you can watch the echo sounder until it reaches the pre-planned reading, and take a visual bearing or two to cross the contour line to complete the fix (see chart below).

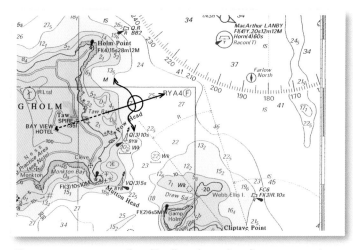

There are many sources of position lines: here a transit crosses a contour

The paperwork

Over centuries, navigators have developed a universal shorthand for writing information on a chart.

Position

+ A dead reckoning position or **DR** is represented by a cross.

△ An estimated position or **EP** is represented by a triangle.

⊙ A fixed position or **fix** is represented by a circle.

Time

The boat's position shown on the chart is only valid at one particular time. Any position should be marked with the time to which it relates.

Position lines

The standard symbol for a position line is an arrowhead.

A visual bearing or transit has an arrowhead on the end pointing away from the landmark.

Any other position line has an arrowhead on each end.

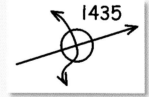

Chapter 5: **Tides**

Anyone who has spent more than a few hours at the seaside in the UK or the Atlantic coast of Europe will have seen the effect of tides. Sandcastles built on the beach in the morning are washed away a few hours later, while fishing boats that were level with the quayside at lunchtime may be several feet below it by evening.

The constantly-changing water level is obviously important to navigators. Rocks which are safely underwater at high water may become dangerously shallow as the sea level falls – and may be visible as useful landmarks a few hours later.

No less significant is the fact that raising and lowering sea level involves moving vast quantities of water from place to place.

The huge amount of energy required to achieve all this comes mainly from the gravitational pull of the sun and moon.

The mechanics of how these tide-raising forces create the tides that we see on the Earth's surface are complex, but they produce some quite simple and predictable rhythms:

■ (Fig 1) A daily rhythm, caused by the rotation of the Earth, in which the water level at any particular place rises and falls twice in just over 24 hours.

■ (Fig 2) A monthly rhythm, in which spring tides (with higher-than-average high waters and lower-than-average low waters) occur at times of full and new moon. In between, at times of quarter moon, we see neap tides, with lower-than-average high waters and higher-than-average low waters.

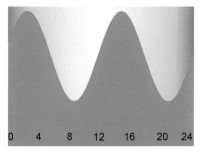

Fig 1: A daily rhythm

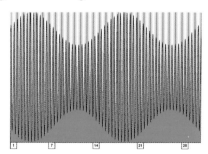

Fig 2: The monthly rhythm

Sea level

Land maps often refer to mean sea level, but at sea we use several different terms to refer to the constantly-changing water level (Fig 1).

Lowest Astronomical Tide (LAT) is the lowest level to which the tide is expected to fall, based on astronomical predictions. It is particularly significant to navigators because it is the reference level or Chart Datum below which charted depths are measured.

Highest Astronomical Tide (HAT) is the exact opposite: it is the highest level to which the tide is expected to rise.

Between these two are various other levels:-

Mean High Water Springs – the level of high water at an average spring tide.

Mean High Water Neaps – the level of high water at an average neap tide.

Mean Low Water Neaps – the level of low water at an average neap tide.

Mean Low Water Springs – the level of low water at an average spring tide.

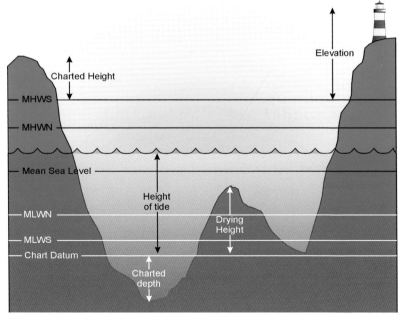

Fig 1: The actual depth of water or height of an object almost never corresponds to the depth or height shown on the chart

An Introduction to Navigation

So how deep is it?

The depths shown on the chart are measured from the Lowest Astronomical Tide, so they err on the side of pessimism. But if we want to know the actual depth at any particular spot, at any particular time, we need to know the height of the water level above LAT (see chart below).

■ Where the sea bed is below chart datum, the actual depth is the height of tide **plus** the charted depth.

■ Where the sea bed is above chart datum (on a green bit of an Admiralty chart), the actual depth is the height of tide **minus** the charted height.

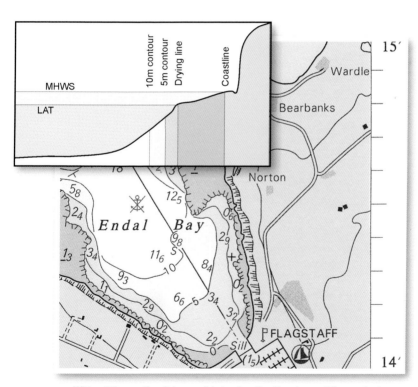

With a little practice, it is possible to visualise the shape of the sea bed by looking at the contours and spot depths

Tide tables

Tide tables give the predicted height of tide. They are available from many different sources, and vary in their coverage and detail, depending on where you find them. Many local newspapers give the times of high water for one or two days at their biggest local port. At the other extreme, the Admiralty Tide Tables gives information for every day of the year, and in such detail that you can find the height of tide at any time and at any port or harbour around the British Isles.

As well as these paper-based sources of information, many chart plotters include tide predictions as do websites such as http://easytide.ukho.gov.uk (Fig 1).

Amongst small-boat navigators, however, the most popular sources of tidal information are almanacs, such as *Reeds Nautical Almanac*. Reeds presents data in much the same format as the Admiralty Tide Tables.

Fig 1: Most chart plotters now include tide prediction software

Tide tables – a standard port

Suppose that we are intending to visit Namley on September 16 (Fig 2), and want to know whether it will be safe to cross the bar across the entrance – shown on the chart as having some parts that are 0.3m above chart datum.

The first step is to turn to the pages that deal with Namley Harbour, and find the column for September.

SEPTEMBER

	Time	m
16	0039	1.2
	0708	3.1
M	1322	1.1
	1954	3.3

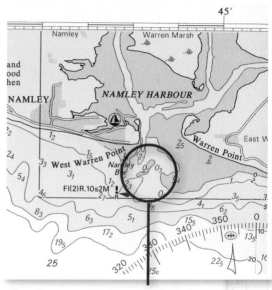

Each day has its own block of information.
For September 16 it says:-

0039	1.2
0708	3.1
1322	1.1
1954	3.3

Fig 2: Many natural harbours are effectively closed at low water by shallow sand bars

The first column of numbers gives the times of High and Low waters, while the second column gives the corresponding heights.

So we can immediately see that high waters (HW) are at 07:08 and 19:54, with heights of 3.1m and 3.3m respectively, while low waters (LW) are at 00:39 and 13:22, with heights of 1.2m and 1.1m.

It's important to read the note in the corner of the page which says "For Summer Time add ONE hour in non-shaded areas". In other words, high water is at 08:08 BST and 20:54 BST, while low water is at 01:39 BST and 14:22 BST.

> TIME ZONE **UT**
> For Summer Time add ONE
> hour in **non-shaded areas**

Tide tables – times between high and low

This doesn't really answer the question of whether it is safe to cross the 0.3m drying heights on Namley Bar.

At 14:22 BST, at low water (LW), with 1.1m of tide, there will be only 1.1 – 0.3 = 0.8m of water – enough for a dinghy, but not much more.

At 20:54 BST, at high water (HW), the tide will have risen to 3.3m above chart datum, so there should be 3.3 – 0.3 = 3.0m – enough for a small ship.

The tide doesn't rise and fall at a constant rate. At low water (LW), it starts rising – slowly at first, but increasingly quickly. Then, as it approaches high water (HW), it starts slowing down again.

In most places a graph of the changing height of tide would look something like the bell-shaped curve in the illustration. Yachtsmen's almanacs and Admiralty Tide Tables include tidal curves alongside the tide tables for each major port, making it reasonably easy to estimate the height of tide at times between high and low water (Fig 1).

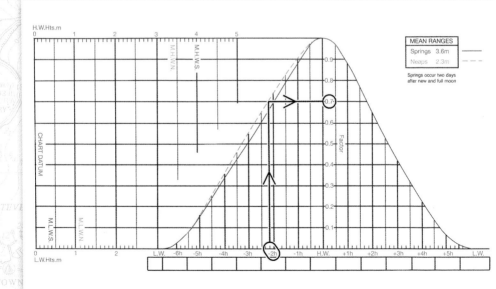

Fig 1: Tide curves allow the height of tide to be calculated for times between high and low water

The published graph actually includes two curves – one for spring tides, and the other for neaps. Use whichever is most appropriate for the tide on that particular day, or estimate a curve between the two for days that are midway between springs and neaps.

Suppose, for instance, we have narrowed down our expected time of arrival at Namley to about 18:45.

We've already found that high water (HW) at Namley on that day is at 20:54, so 18:45 is about 2 hours 10 minutes before HW. Across the bottom of the graph, there is a scale of time, shown as hours before and after HW, while up the centre of the graph is another scale labelled Factor.

From the graph we can see that 2 hours 10 minutes before HW corresponds to a factor of 0.7. This means that at 18:45, the tide should have risen 0.7 of the way from low water to high.

■ LW was 1.1m, and HW is 3.3m
  so the difference between the two (the range of tide) is 2.2m.

■ 0.7 of 2.2 is 1.5m
  so at 18:45, the tide should have risen 1.5 from LW.

■ LW was 1.1m,
  so the Height of Tide at 1845 should be 1.1m + 1.5m = 2.6m above chart datum.

■ We are interested in a spot where the sea bed is 0.3m above chart datum
  so the depth of water over Namley Bar should be 2.6m – 0.3m = 2.3m.

Tide tables – heights between high and low

It's often even more useful to be able to do the calculation backwards to find out when there **will** be enough water (Fig 1).

Suppose, we need at least 1.7m of water.

- We are interested in a spot where the sea bed is 0.3m above chart datum so we need 1.7m + 0.3m = 2.0m height of tide.

- LW was 1.1m,
  so we want the tide to have risen 2.0m – 1.1m = 0.9m from LW.

- LW was 1.1m, and HW is 3.3m
  so the difference between the two (the range of tide) is 2.2m.

- 0.9m is 0.4 of the range
  so we can cross the bar whenever the factor is bigger than 0.4.

- Looking at the curve, this appears to be 3h45m before HW.
  HW is at 20:54, so we should be able to cross the bar any time after 20:54 – 3:45 = 17:09.

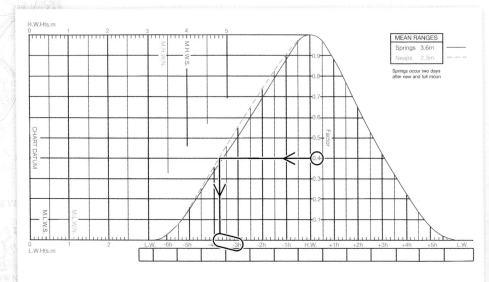

Fig 1: It's often useful to be able to do the tidal calculation backwards to find out when the tide will reach a certain height

An Introduction to Navigation

Tide tables – the rule of twelfths

More basic tide tables may not include the tidal curve. Fortunately, though, the graph for most places is similar to Namley's bell-shaped curve, so we can use a fairly simple rule of thumb (Fig 2).

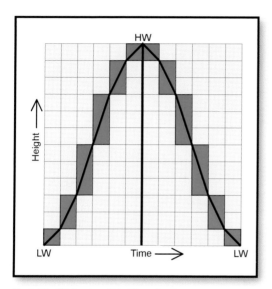

Fig 2: The "Rule of twelfths" is a simple way of estimating the height of tide between high and low water

It's called the "Rule of Twelfths", because it says

- In the **first** hour after low water, the tide rises one **twelfth** of its range

- In the **second** hour after low water, the tide rises **two twelfths** of its range

- In the **third** hour after low water, the tide rises **three twelfths** of its range

- In the **third** hour before high water, the tide rises **three twelfths** of its range

- In the **second** hour before high water, the tide rises **two twelfths** of its range

- In the **last** hour before high water, the tide rises **one twelfth** of its range.

It's important to be aware, that some places, especially where there are islands close to the coast, have tidal curves that are quite severely distorted.

Tide tables – a secondary port

Even such substantial books as Reeds Almanac and the Admiralty Tide Tables cannot include full tables for every port.

The solution is provided by difference tables such as the one for Port Rampton (Fig 1).

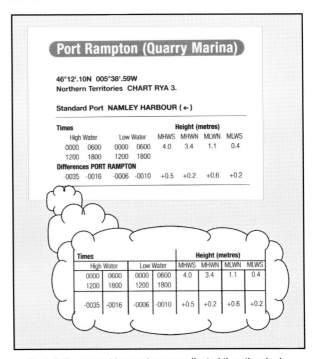

Fig 1: Difference tables are less complicated than they look

It tells us how the tides at Port Rampton differ from those at the nearest standard port – in this case, Namley. It's really a very simple table, consisting of one row of information, divided into eight columns. It just looks confusing because the column headings take up more space than the information itself!

The first two columns deal with the time of high water, and tell us that:

- If HW Namley is at midnight or mid-day (00:00 or 12:00), then HW Port Rampton is 35 minutes earlier (-00:35).
- If HW Namley is at 06:00 or 18:00, then HW Port Rampton is 16 minutes earlier (-00:16).

An Introduction to Navigation

The next two columns deal with the time of low water, and tell us that:

■ If LW Namley is at midnight or mid-day (00:00 or 12:00), then LW Port Rampton is six minutes earlier (-00:06).

■ If LW Namley is at 06:00 or 18:00, then HW Port Rampton is 10 minutes earlier (-00:10).

The third pair of columns deal with the height of high water, and tell us that:

■ If HW Namley is at 4.0m then HW Port Rampton is 0.5m higher (+0.5).

■ If HW Namley is at 3.4m then HW Port Rampton is 0.2m higher (+0.2).

The final pair of columns treat low water in exactly the same way, telling us that:

■ If LW Namley is at 1.1m then LW Port Rampton is 0.6m higher (+0.6).

■ If LW Namley is at 0.4m then LW Port Rampton is 0.2m higher (+0.2).

Knowing that HW Namley is expected to be at 1954 GMT, we can look at the difference tables and see that:

■ If HW Namley is at midnight, HW Port Rampton is 35 minutes earlier (-00:35) but if HW Namley is at 18:00, HW Port Rampton is 16 minutes earlier (-00:16).

■ HW Namley is at 19:54, which is about one third of the way between 18:00 and midnight.

■ So the difference for Port Rampton is about one third of the way between 16 minutes and 35 minutes: say 22 minutes earlier than at Namley.

■ So HW Port Rampton is at 19:54 – 22 = 19:32.

■ To complete the job add an hour to convert to BST 19:32 + 01:00 = 20:32 BST.

The height calculation is similar. The difference tables tell us that:

■ If HW Namley is at 4.0m, HW Port Rampton is 0.5m higher (+0.5). but if HW Namley is at 3.4m, HW Port Rampton is only 0.2m higher (+0.2).

■ In this case HW Namley is 3.3m, which is as close to 3.4m as makes no difference.

■ So the height of HW Port Rampton is 3.3m + 0.2m = 3.5m.

Having worked out the time and height of high water, the procedure for finding the corresponding information for low water is exactly the same.

Graphs are rarely provided for secondary ports, but for most practical purposes, the graph for the nearest standard port will do.

Tidal Streams

Raising and lowering sea level by several metres and over large areas involves moving vast quantities of water from place to place, creating currents known as tidal streams.

Tidal streams can reach speeds of ten knots or more, but this is unusual. More often they flow at a relatively docile one or two knots, but even that is quite enough to have a significant navigational effect.

Navigating on tidal water is like walking on one of those moving corridors that they have in airports. If you stop, you are carried along on a moving carpet of water. If you sail or motor in the same direction as the tidal stream, you will move faster across the ground than through the water, but if you turn round and head into the tidal stream, you will slow down.

Navigating across a tidal stream is more complicated. If you set off by heading straight for your intended destination, the tidal stream will carry you sideways (Fig 1).

The obvious alternative, particularly if you can see your destination, is to alter course to aim straight at it. For a little while, all will seem well, but the tidal stream will still be sweeping you sideways, so you will have to alter course more and more up-tide.

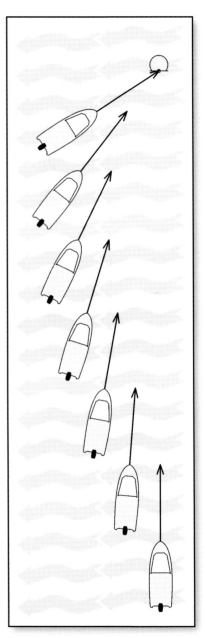

Fig 1: Navigating in tidal stream is not just a matter of aiming for your destination

A much more efficient alternative is to allow for the tidal stream at the outset. There are various ways of calculating a course to steer to allow for the effect of a tidal stream, but these are outside the scope of this book (see the RYA Navigation Handbook). For passages lasting less than about an hour, however, there are three simple tricks that you can use.

1 When you can see your destination. As you set off, look beyond your destination, for some landmark in the distance. Anything will do, so long as it is beyond your destination, is visually distinctive, and is stationary (Fig 1). Then, instead of simply aiming at your destination, adjust your course so as to keep your destination in line with your landmark. In effect, what you've done is set up an impromptu transit (see page 38) and are steering to stay on the transit line.

Fig 1: By keeping the buoy lined up with the dark trees beyond it, we can be sure that we are travelling straight towards it, even if the boat is actually pointing in a different direction!

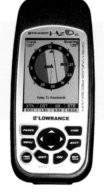

2 Uses the GPS waypoint functions. Having set your destination as a Go To waypoint, you can counter the effect of a tidal stream – over short distances – by keeping the cross track error close to zero.

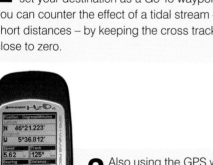

3 Also using the GPS waypoint functions – involves adjusting your course (the direction you are steering) so that your track (the direction you are moving) matches the bearing to waypoint (the direction you want to go).

An Introduction to Navigation

Predicting tidal streams

Tidal streams generally flow into and out of harbours and river estuaries, roughly parallel to coastlines, though this simple picture is complicated by the presence of bays, headlands, and islands. Fortunately, because tidal streams are created by the same astronomical forces as tides, they share a common rhythm. This means that tidal stream information can be referred to the time of High Water at a nearby standard port. It's not unusual, for instance, to find pilot books giving advice such as "Leave as soon as the stream turns north at about HW Dover +0430" (In other words, leave four and a half hours after HW Dover).

There are two main sources of more detailed tidal stream information:

1. Tidal diamonds

Tidal diamonds refer to diamond-shaped symbols that are printed on Admiralty charts in magenta ink (Fig 1). Other publishers use other symbols, but the principle is the same.

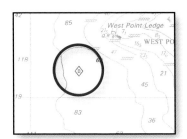

Fig 1: A tidal diamond is simply a reference point for tidal stream data

Each diamond identifies a particular spot on the chart, for which the tidal stream information is given in a table of data, somewhere else on the chart (Fig 2).

In the table, the information for each diamond is divided into three columns, and 13 rows. Each row corresponds to a particular hour before or after High Water.

Tidal Streams referred to HW at VICTORIA

Hours	Geographical Position		⬨ A 46°20ʹ5 N 5 50·0W		⬨ B 46°20ʹ6 N 6 18·4W		⬨ C 46°11ʹ2 N 5 43·2W	
	streams (degrees)	ng tides (knots) / ap tides (knots)						
Before High Water 6			−6	110	1·8 0·8	158	1·0 0·6	189	1·7 0·9
5			−5	108	1·0 0·5	153	1·7 0·8	192	1·1 0·6
4			−4	026	0·4 0·2	159	2·8 1·5	290	0·6 0·4
3			−3	297	1·4 0·7	154	3·9 2·0	359	1·5 0·8
2			−2	278	2·0 1·1	165	3·2 1·7	004	1·8 0·9
1			−1	274	1·7 0·8	173	2·4 1·3	007	1·4 0·7
High Water			0	271	1·1 0·5	186	1·2 0·7	010	0·9 0·5

Fig 2: A panel on the chart gives tidal stream data at each of several tidal diamonds

The first column shows the direction towards which the tide is flowing; the second shows its rate (in knots) at a typical spring tide, while the final column shows the rate at that stage in a neap tide.

In Fig 2, the section referring to tidal diamond B shows that three hours before HW Victoria, the tidal stream at that particular tidal diamond is flowing in a 154°(T) direction at 3.9 knots at a typical spring tide, and at 2.0 knots at a typical neap tide.

2. Tidal stream atlases

Tidal stream atlases provide the same data but in a sequence of 12 or 13 small charts, each showing the situation at a particular moment in the tidal cycle (Fig 3). Thick arrows represent strong tidal streams, with thinner arrows depicting weaker ones, and numbers such as 20.39 provide greater precision.

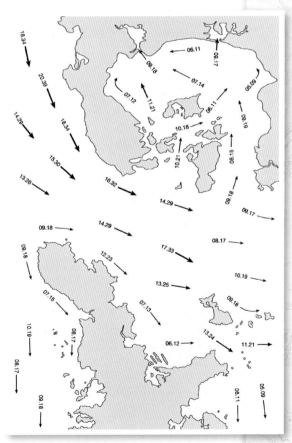

In this example 18.34 means that the neap rate is 1.8 knots and the spring rate is 3.4 knots, at the position indicated by the full stop. The full stops, incidentally, are usually at the same places as the tidal diamonds on the corresponding chart, so the "20,39" just below the top right hand corner of the tidal stream atlas corresponds exactly with the tidal diamond B in the chart extract in Fig 1 and Fig 2.

Fig 3: A tidal stream atlas shows the changing pattern of tidal streams, with a separate chart for every hour of the tidal cycle

Chapter 6: **Buoys**

Buoys are sometimes described as signposts of the sea. It's not a very good comparison because – unlike signposts – they don't tell you how to get somewhere. They are more like the bollards that mark the edges of dangerous bends on country roads.

Fig 1: Beacons are posts or towers standing on the sea bed, rather than floating on the surface, but they conform to the same shape and colour code as buoys, and serve the same purpose

There are three main groups of buoys and beacons:-

1. Cardinal Marks

2. Lateral Marks

3. Miscellaneous Marks

1. Cardinal marks

Cardinal marks are always black and yellow, with topmarks consisting of two black cones. They are positioned around hazards such as sandbanks, rocks, and wrecks, and are named after the four cardinal points of the compass:

A **North Cardinal Mark** is placed to the north of the hazard, and has relatively clear water to the north of it.

Remember it by thinking of the cones pointing **up** to the top of the chart (north) and **up** to the black bit of the buoy. If it has a light (not all do), it will be a continuous sequence of flashes at about the same speed (or slower) as those of a car's direction indicators.

A **South Cardinal Mark** is placed to the south of the hazard, and has relatively clear water to the south of it.

Think of the cones pointing **down** to the southern edge of the chart and **down** to the black bit of the buoy. If it has a light, it will flash at about the same speed as a north cardinal, but the flashes will be in groups of six, with a distinctive long flash at the end of each group. Think of the six flashes as indicating that it is at six o'clock relative to the hazard.

An **East Cardinal Mark** is placed to the east of the hazard, and has relatively clear water to the east of it.

Remember the colour scheme by thinking of the cones indicating the black part top and bottom mark, and visualize the overall shape of the two cones as an egg-shape or a lower-case "e". If it has a light, it will flash in groups of three: think of it as being at three o'clock relative to the hazard.

A **West Cardinal Mark** is placed to the west of the hazard, and has relatively clear water to the west of it.

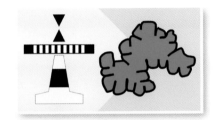

Following the pattern set by the others, think of the cones indicating the black part of the mark, while the top mark can be remembered as a letter W turned on its side. If it has a light, it follows the "clock" rule by flashing groups of nine flashes to correspond with its position at nine o'clock relative to the hazard.

2. Lateral marks

Lateral marks often (but not always) mark the edges of reasonably well defined channels, and are named port-hand or starboard-hand according to the side on which they are intended to be passed when you are approaching or entering harbour, or when going clockwise around a continent.

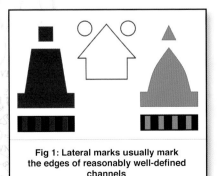

Fig 1: Lateral marks usually mark the edges of reasonably well-defined channels

Around Europe and most of the rest of the world (not the USA), **Port hand marks** are can-shaped (cylindrical) or have can-shaped top marks, and are red. If a port-hand buoy has a light, it too is always red (Fig 1).

Starboard hand marks are conical or have conical top marks, and are green. If a starboard-hand buoy has a light, it too is always green.

When leaving harbour, heading out of a river, or going anti-clockwise round a continent, your direction of travel is reversed, but no-one comes out to switch all the buoys round for you! This means that port hand buoys have to be left to starboard when leaving, or going anti-clockwise.

The into harbour and clockwise rules are both straightforward enough in themselves, but there are inevitably places where they contradict each other, particularly at major headlands, large estuaries (such as the Clyde) and in the vicinity of islands.

Where there is a significant risk of ambiguity, or where there is a particularly abrupt change, the direction of buoyage is marked on charts with a large magenta arrow symbol.

Where a channel forks, the buoy at the centre of the fork has to have a split personality, because it has to be treated as a starboard hand buoy by vessels taking the left fork, but as a port hand buoy for those taking the right fork (Fig 2).

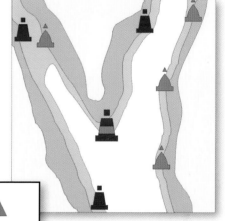

Fig 2: Where a channel forks, the buoy at the centre of the fork has to have a split personality

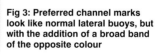

Fig 3: Preferred channel marks look like normal lateral buoys, but with the addition of a broad band of the opposite colour

In practice, the usual solution is to use a Cardinal Buoy, but the IALA convention includes preferred channel marks to deal with the situation.

As can be seen in Fig 3, they look very much like normal lateral buoys, but with the addition of a broad band of the opposite colour, and lights which flash a distinctive 2+1 rhythm. They may look complicated, but the simple rule is that if you want to follow the preferred channel, treat each one as though it were a normal lateral mark of the same shape and colour, without the band.

3. Miscellaneous marks

The miscellaneous group includes three completely different kinds of mark.

Safe water marks

A safe water mark is positioned where there is safe water all around it. Of course, the presence of a safe water mark implies rather more than just an absence of hazard: it may mark the beginning or centreline of a channel. The buoy itself can be spherical or pillar-shaped, but it is always red and white and usually has a single red ball top mark.

Isolated danger marks

An isolated danger mark also has safe water all around it, but the mark itself is positioned right on top of a hazard of relatively small size, such as a wreck or a pinnacle of rock. By their very nature, Isolated danger marks are seldom found in deep water, so they are often in the form of beacon towers or beacons, rather than buoys.

The distinctive features of an isolated danger mark are its red and black colour, and the two black balls of its top mark. When lit, isolated danger marks show two white flashes.

Special marks

Special marks are generally the least significant of the IALA marks.

They can be used to mark areas set aside for military exercises, survey work, dumping grounds, cables and pipelines, recommended anchorages, recreational areas (such as waterski areas) and as yacht racing marks.

A special mark is always yellow, and if it has a top mark it is in the form of a saltire (multiplication sign). The light, if it has one, is always yellow, but the buoy or mark itself can be any shape. If it is can shaped or conical, though, it is best to treat it as though it were a port or starboard hand buoy respectively.

Charted information

Lighthouses

On charts, lighthouses are represented by a black star-shaped symbol and a magenta teardrop. Smaller light structures, such as those on jetty heads are marked by a smaller star, without the hollow centre, but still with the magenta flash (Fig 1). Either type may be accompanied by abbreviated information including:

1. Its character or rhythm
2. Its colour
3. Its period (the time it takes to complete one complete sequence of flashes) (Fig 2)
4. Its elevation (height above MHWS)
5. Its nominal range
6. Details of any associated fog signal

Fig 1: A lighthouse is represented by a black star-shaped symbol and a magenta "teardrop"

Fixed	F	Unchanging	
Flashing	Fl	Less light than dark	
Group flashing	Fl (2)	(for example)	
Long flashing	LFl	Flash lasting more than 2 sec	
Quick	Q	50-79 flashes per min	
Group quick	Q (9)	(for example)	
Isophase	Iso	Equal light and dark	
Occulting	Oc	More light than dark	
Group occulting	Oc (3)	(for example)	

← Period →

Fig 2: Every light has a distinctive characteristic: these are some of the commonest ones

The colour is usually omitted if it is a white light. Other information is selectively omitted from smaller scale charts, but the colour and rhythm are usually retained.

Buoys and beacons

Buoys and beacons are shown as symbols representing the general shape of the buoy or beacon and its top mark, with a small circle at the base of the symbol indicating its actual position. A letter or letters below the symbol indicate its colour. If it is lit, the symbol is supplemented by a magenta flash, and a label indicating the rhythm and period. The range and elevation are not shown, and the period is often omitted from smaller-scale charts.

Chapter 7: **Pilotage**

Navigation is not just about where we are, or where we're going: it's also about not bumping into things.

In open water, not bumping into things is relatively easy, compared with the job of getting from A to B, but there comes a time – particularly at the beginning and end of a passage – when the priorities change. In harbour, where the water is shallower, the hazards closer, and conventional navigation is too slow and cumbersome, we need a different kind of navigation, using a handful of short-range, high-speed techniques known as pilotage.

Finding your way into an artificial harbour may involve nothing more sophisticated than aiming between two pier heads.

Only marginally more complex is the situation found in some rivers, where the deep water channel is lined with moorings. Following the channel is just a matter of following the line of clear water. But it sometimes comes as a surprise, to novice navigators, to find that following a buoyed channel isn't quite as obvious as following the cat's eyes along a motorway: the buoys may be several miles apart, or there may be so many of them that it is not at all obvious which is the next one to head for.

Buoy hopping

Following a channel by steering from buoy to buoy is a perfectly legitimate pilotage technique, so long as you guard against a couple of pitfalls.

The first is the risk of heading for the wrong mark.

Approaching Rozelle Cove (see chart opposite), for instance, the Fairway Buoy is an obvious waypoint.

From there, the route to the Marina passes close to a starboard-hand post (green, with a triangular topmark) then dog-legs north-eastward before turning northwards again to pass between three more starboard-hand posts and their port-hand counterparts (red with cylindrical topmarks).

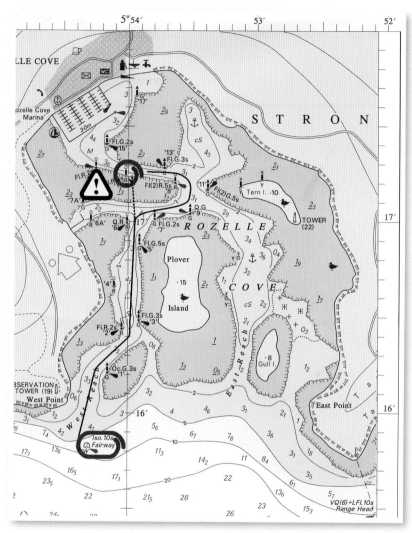

The most obvious buoy may not always be the right one!

After passing the third of the red posts, there is another red post almost directly ahead, a quarter of a mile away – but heading straight for it would take us right over the rocky ledge that the posts are supposed to mark.

The chart shows that the safe channel turns almost 90 degrees to starboard at this point.

The first line of defence against this trap is preparation: make a note of the approximate bearing (direction) and distance of each mark from the one before. Armed with that information, you should know exactly where to look for each mark before you arrive at the one before it. If the worst comes to the worst, you can always turn the boat onto the required bearing, and be confident that the mark you are looking for will be somewhere in front.

The most subtle trap for buoy-hoppers is caused by wind and tide.

Suppose, for instance, that we are pottering inside Namley Harbour (Fig 1), aiming to head from the South Cardinal buoy to the red port-hand buoy about 700 metres to the east of it.

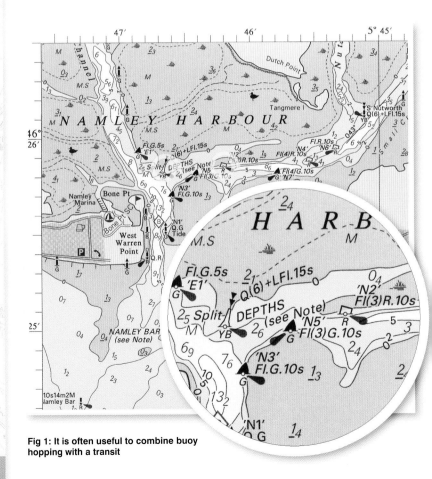

Fig 1: It is often useful to combine buoy hopping with a transit

An Introduction to Navigation

Aiming straight for the buoy could be a mistake. With our speed constrained by a harbour speed limit, and a strong tidal stream sluicing through the harbour entrance, we'd be pushed sideways.

Simply altering course to aim for the buoy isn't enough. The trick is to use the transit technique described in Chapter 4, by looking beyond the buoy, for some more distant landmark beyond it. On the chart, the most obvious candidate appears to be another red buoy, but in real life you might well choose a moored boat or a distinctive bush on the shoreline.

Keeping the buoy and your chosen landmark in line guarantees that you are moving in a straight line, and in the direction you intended.

Transits

Transits are such a powerful pilotage tool that in many harbours, distinctive marks have been set up to form leading lines (Fig 2).

Fig 2: Transits are such a powerful pilotage tool that in many harbours, distinctive marks have been set up to form leading lines

Steering towards the leading marks, the secret of staying on the line is to keep the marks in line with each other by following the front mark. In other words, if the mark nearest to you appears to be sliding to the left of the more distant mark, steer to port, and vice versa.

Coming out of harbour, with the marks astern, the opposite applies: you follow the rear mark, steering to port if it drifts off to the left of the nearer mark.

Planning pilotage

It's no good getting to the entrance of an unfamiliar harbour before you start thinking about how you are going to find your way in. Pilotage is the purest, simplest kind of navigation there is, but it only works if you have done all the preparation.

1. Calculate the height of tide.

2. Use charts and pilot books to get a feel for the place.

3. Make notes in a form that you can understand, using directions, distances, and descriptions: "Steer north 0.5mile to Green conical post" is much more informative than "Head for No. 5 pile".

4. Have a back-up plan, if possible, in case you can't identify a leading mark or can't find a buoy.

5. Know how close it is safe to go: many novice navigators start worrying because they can't see a buoy when they are a mile offshore, when they could safely approach to half a mile, and be able to see it easily.

Pilot books

Pilot books are produced by a number of commercial publishers, and vary widely in style and quality: some are little more than tourist guides aimed at visitors who happen to travel by boat, while others are packed with useful information, including photographs of key landmarks and even "potted" pilotage plans. It is worth being aware, though, that even the best of commercial pilot books are seldom bang up to date.

TOM CUNLIFFE
The Shell Channel Pilot

Putting it into practice

If you have made a perfect plan, putting it into practice is no more than a matter of following the plan. In reality, though, things seldom happen that way!

If possible, it pays to work as a team, in which the helm takes responsibility for keeping the boat on track, leaving the navigator free to concentrate on locating and identifying the buoys, beacons, and land marks. Then, as they approach a turning point, the navigator advises the helm what to do next – whether it is "aim for that buoy" or "keep the two yellow posts in line".

Having altered course, the navigator's first move must always be to check that the helm is doing what they were asked to do – that they are aiming for the right buoy, or that they really are following a transit, rather than aiming at one of the marks. Then the navigator can turn their attention to the next set of marks.

Chapter 8: **Passage planning**

The freedom to set off into the blue yonder is, for many people, one of the great attractions of boating. But any journey – even one as simple as walking from one room of your home to another – involves some kind of planning. Boating is no exception.

- What are you hoping to achieve?

- What are your limitations?

- What hazards might you encounter?

- What is available to help?

- What route will you take?

SOLAS requirement

The International Safety of Life at Sea (SOLAS) convention requires those in charge of all vessels – including pleasure craft, and regardless of size – to prepare a passage plan before proceeding to sea.

The UK's Maritime and Coastguard Agency (MCA) suggests that a passage plan for small craft should consider:

1. The weather forecast.
2. Tidal predictions.
3. The limitations of the boat and crew.
4. Navigational dangers.
5. A contingency plan.

The plan does not have to be in writing, but the MCA suggests that someone ashore should be aware of plans and know what to do if they are worried about you.

Practical factors

Objectives

The objectives are the most personal of the passage planning factors. It is entirely up to you and your crew whether your objective is to catch a fish, visit the D-Day invasion beaches, or see how fast you can get from A to B ... or any of the countless other things that you might do with a boat!

Of course, there will be factors that limit your freedom of choice...

Constraints

The most important constraints are almost always the crew and the boat. A trip that might be exciting for a crew of fit young adults could be unpleasant or dangerous for an elderly couple, whilst a pleasant day out for the elderly couple might be boring for a young family. By the same token small boats are generally better suited to short passages in sheltered waters. Some very small boats have crossed oceans, but doing so has almost always called for special skill or courage on the part of their crews.

Other constraints include things such as:

- Fuel capacity and consumption.
- Sunrise and sunset.
- Weather forecast.
- Tides and tidal streams.
- Locks, swing bridges or access to a slipway.

Fuel capacity and consumption

Fuel capacity and consumption are crucial importance for any motor boat, and can be significant for a sailing boat – particularly when faced with light winds and strong tidal streams.

As a rule of thumb, a diesel engine burns about a gallon of fuel per hour for every 20hp. So a 200hp diesel, running flat out, will burn about 10 gallons per hour.

Petrol engines are less predictable, but as a rough rule they produce about 12-14hp per gallon per hour.

Throttling back produces huge fuel savings, usually without sacrificing much speed. As another rule of thumb, a 10% reduction in engine speed produces a 25% reduction in fuel consumption (Fig 1).

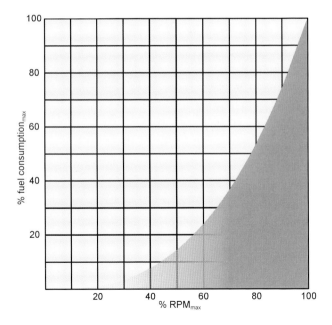

Fig 1: Fuel consumption increases dramatically as the engine speed rises and drops dramatically if you throttle back

An Introduction to Navigation

Sunrise and sunset

Being at sea at night can be a magical experience. On the other hand, operating a boat is more difficult in the dark, and everyone is more prone to cold, tiredness, and seasickness at night.

But nightfall need not catch you unawares: the times of sunset and sunrise are published in many newspapers, and on many web pages. At sea, they are also available on many GPS sets and in most yachtsmen's almanacs.

Weather forecast

We all love to mock the weather forecast, and it is certainly true that weather forecasts should still be regarded as predictions rather than promises. But the weather can make such a big difference to a passage that it would be foolish to ignore forecasts, particularly when they warn of strong winds or poor visibility.

The main source of weather information around the UK coast is the shipping forecast, issued by the Meteorological Office four times a day and broadcast by the BBC on Radio 4. Twice a day, it is supplemented by the Inshore Waters forecast, giving more detail of coastal waters. Both forecasts are available on various websites (including www.metoffice.gov.uk and www.bbc.co.uk), from various fax and telephone services, and from notice boards at marinas and sailing clubs.

Extracts of these forecasts are also broadcast by the Coastguard on marine VHF channels.

Tides

Some marinas have cills, designed to maintain a minimum depth within the marina even when the tide falls. In such places, the tide sets absolute limits to the times at which it is possible to enter or leave the marina (Fig 1).

Many natural harbours have a shallow bar – a natural version of the marina cill – across their entrances.

Fig 1: A cill traps water and boats in the inner harbour when the tide falls

Tidal streams

The effect of tidal streams on a slow boat is obvious: if your boat does five knots through the water, and you have a two knot tidal stream, you will travel at seven knots with the tide in your favour, and only three knots if you to fight it. And if you are trying to sail across it, you'll have to steer almost 25 degrees up-tide to counter its effect.

Tidal streams are particularly pronounced around headlands and through narrow channels, which are sometimes known as tidal gates because the streams may be so strong that slow boats can only get past at certain times.

For a high-speed motor boat, the effect of the same two-knot tidal stream is less marked: with a boat speed of 25 knots you will achieve 23 knots even if the tide is against you, while the offset to counter a cross tide will be only five degrees.

But for both groups, fast or slow, the sea state may be important – and may be dramatically affected by the tidal stream. If the wind and tide are in roughly the same direction, the waves are generally longer, lower, and less likely to break than if the wind and tide are against each other.

For a sailing boat, it is almost always worth planning a passage so as to have the tidal stream in your favour as much as possible. The navigator of a planing motor cruiser, on the other hand, may want to think about making an upwind passage against the tidal stream in order to take advantage of the smoother water when wind and tide are together.

Hazards

Whether something is a constraint or a hazard is pretty academic: a patch of sand with less water over it than you need to float your boat is generally something to be avoided, whichever category you choose to put it in!

Typical hazards include:-

- Rocks and shallows
- Rough water
- Adverse tidal streams
- Adverse weather
- Dense or fast-moving traffic
- Prohibited areas

Aids

Aids include all the things that might help you to achieve your objective, including favourable tides, good weather, landmarks and seamarks, as well as equipment such as GPS, and all the techniques in this book.

Just because an aid exists doesn't mean that you have to use it: it is pointless to detour round a buoy if you can safely cut straight across the shallow patch that it is supposed to mark.

On the other hand, it is equally silly to ignore a perfectly good aid just because it isn't exactly where you might want it. For instance, it's a lot nicer (and more accurate) to steer a small boat by eye than by compass, so it might be worth adapting your route to aim straight for a prominent landmark, rather than steering by compass towards a bare horizon.

The route

The pages of a ship's deck log are traditionally headed "From" and "Towards", rather than "From" and "To", because it is tempting fate to suggest that there is any certainty about your destination. But times and practices change.

There is nothing to be lost by drawing your route onto a chart or storing it in an electronic chart plotter, and a lot to be gained.

For the electronic navigator, waypoints are essential if you want to use the "navigate" functions of a GPS or chart plotter, such as range and bearing to waypoint or cross track error. Even for traditional navigators, it is easier to monitor progress and recognise when things are going wrong if your route is marked on the chart.

Do:	Don't:
■ Check that the straight-line track between waypoints doesn't pass uncomfortably close to any hazards	■ Aim to pass closer to hazards than the accuracy of your navigation
■ If possible, use landmarks as "aiming points" rather than steering by compass	■ Re-use old waypoints or waypoints from a published list "just because they are there"
■ If possible, put waypoints where they can be checked by eye	■ Take a "battleship sweep" around headlands by placing one waypoint miles offshore in order to save the trouble of plotting two or three waypoints closer in
■ If your GPS requires waypoints to be entered by latitude and longitude, double check each one: and make sure that the ranges and bearings from each waypoint to the next are what you expected them to be.	■ Use the exact position of a buoy or beacon as a waypoint (you might hit it!)

Bolt-holes

For all but the shortest of passages, it is worth looking at possible bolt-holes that you can divert to if something goes wrong, or that you can call into to wait for a lock to open or for the tide to turn. On more ambitious passages, or with an unfamiliar boat or crew it may even be worth adapting your route to make sure that suitable bolt-holes are never far away.

Glossary

bar a shallow patch extending across the mouth of a river or harbour

beacons marks that are fixed to the sea bed (see cardinal marks, lateral marks or miscellaneous marks)

bearing the direction of one object from another

breton plotter a particular type of chart plotter (see chart plotter (1))

buoys floating marks (see cardinal marks, lateral marks or miscellaneous marks)

cardinal marks buoys or beacons used to indicate the presence of hazards

cardinal points the four main directions indicated by a traditional mariner's compass (North, South, East, and West)

chart a marine map, in printed or electronic form

chart datum the level below which charted depths are measured (usually but not always the lowest astronomical tide)

chart plotter (1) a device for measuring directions and drawing lines on printed charts

chart plotter (2) a device for displaying electronic charts

cill a wall that retains water in a harbour even when the tide falls

cocked hat a triangle formed by the intersection of three position lines

compass a device for measuring direction in the real world

compass (hand bearing) see hand bearing compass

compass (steering) see steering compass

compass rose a graphic representation of directions on a printed chart, often including an indication of the variation

contour a line joining points of equal height or depth

course direction the vessel is being steered

course made good see track angle

course over ground see track angle

cross track error distance between your present position and the track you intended to follow

datum (chart) see chart datum

datum (horizontal) see horizontal datum

dead reckoning a position calculated using only the course steered and the distance travelled

depths (spot) see spot depths

deviation the difference between magnetic north and north indicated by a magnetic compass

difference tables tables showing the difference between tidal data for a secondary port and a nearby standard port

dividers an instrument used for measuring distances on a printed chart

DR see dead reckoning

drying height the height of the sea bed above chart datum (eg a rock or sandbank that is sometimes covered but sometimes above water)

echo sounder an electronic device for measuring the depth of water, showing the depth on an analogue or digital display

EP see estimated position

equator an imaginary line around the Earth, exactly mid-way between the north and south poles

estimated position a best estimate of a vessel's position: eg a dead reckoning position adjusted to allow for it allows for the effect of wind and tide travelled

fish finder an electronic device for measuring the depth of water and displaying the shape of the sea bed on a graphic display

fix see fixed position

fixed position a position that has been confirmed by measurement (eg by GPS or by compass bearings)

gate (tidal) see tidal gate

Global Positioning System a satellite navigation system in which an on-board or hand-held receiver uses signals from satellites to establish its position and time

go to on a GPS receiver or chart plotter, a simple route from the present position to a single waypoint

GPS see Global Positioning System

ground track see track angle

hand bearing compass a hand-held compass designed for measuring bearings

HAT see highest astronomical tide

heading the direction the vessel happens to be pointing at any given moment

height of tide the height of the sea surface above chart datum

highest astronomical tide the highest level to which the sea surface is expected to rise, based on astronomical factors but assuming standard weather conditions.

horizontal datum the grid of latitude and longitude to which positions are referred

knot a unit of speed equal to one nautical mile per hour

LAT see lowest astronomical tide

lateral marks buoys or beacons used to indicate the edges of a well-defined channel

latitude the distance of a place is its distance from the Equator, expressed as an angle

latitude and longitude see latitude and longitude

leading marks leading lights, marks or lights that have been set up to form a transit to guide vessels along a particular channel

log a mechanical or electronic device for measuring the distance a boat has travelled through the water

longitude the angle between the Prime Meridian and the meridian of the place measured around the Equator in degrees at the centre of the Earth

lowest astronomical tide the lowest level to which the sea surface is expected to fall, based on astronomical factors but assuming standard weather conditions

lubber line a line on a steering compass that represents the boat's centreline or its counterpart on a hand bearing compass

marks see cardinal marks, lateral marks or miscellaneous marks

mean high water neaps the level of high water at an average neap tide

mean high water springs the level of high water at an average spring tide

mean low water neaps the level of low water at an average neap tide

mean low water springs the level of low water at an average spring tide

meridian an imaginary line between the north and south poles

meridian (prime) see prime meridian

MHWN see Mean High Water Neaps

MHWS see Mean High Water Springs

mile (nautical) 1852 metres

mile (sea) a minute of latitude measured at the Earth's surface

miscellaneous marks buoys or beacons used for purposes other than Cardinal marks or Lateral marks

MLWN see Mean Low Water Neaps

MLWS see Mean Low Water Springs

nautical mile see mile (nautical)

neap tide a tide with a smaller range than the tide before or after it

north (compass) the direction of North as indicated by a magnetic compass

north (magnetic) the direction of the Earth's magnetic field: i.e the direction of North as would be indicated by a magnetic compass if there were no other magnetic influences

north (true) the direction towards the Earth's north pole

parallels an imaginary line around the Earth, parallel to the equator

plotter (breton) see breton plotter

plotter (chart) see chart plotter

position line a line (such as a compass bearing) on which a vessel's position is believed to lie

prime meridian the meridian from which longitude is measured (formerly known as the Greenwich Meridian, because it passes through the Greenwich Observatory)

range distance to an object from another (usually from your own position)

range of tide the difference in height between low water and the next or previous high water

rose (compass) see compass rose

rule of twelfths a rule of thumb for estimating the height of tide

scale the ratio between a distance in the real world and the corresponding distance on the chart

sea mile see mile (sea)

secondary port a port for which detailed tide tables are not available, but can be calculated using difference tables

SOLAS Safety of Life at Sea Convention an international agreement setting out various rules concerned with the safety of ships and smaller vessels

spot depths numbers on the navigational chart, showing the depth of the sea bed below chart datum at particular spots

spring tide a tide with a greater range than the tide before or after it

standard port a port for which detailed tide tables are available

steering compass a compass used to measure and monitor the boat's heading

three figure notation a way of expressing direction as an angle measured in degrees, counting clockwise from north

tidal diamonds locations on a chart for which tidal stream data is supplied in tabular form

tidal gate an area where the tidal streams are so strong that it is impractical to proceed against the tide

tidal stream atlas a book showing tidal streams in graphical form

tidal streams the horizontal movement of water associated with the rising and falling tide

tide the rise and fall of sea level caused by astronomical factors such as the gravitational forces of the sun and moon

tide tables tables showing the predicted times and heights of tide

track see track angle

track angle the direction the vessel is actually moving: it is often abbreviated to Track, and can also be known as Ground Track, Course Made Good, or Course over Ground

transit two objects on the same bearing (i.e. they appear to be in line with each other)

variation the difference between true north and magnetic north

wake course see water track

water track the direction the vessel is moving through the water, and is sometimes called the Wake Course

waypoint a fixed position stored in the memory of a GPS receiver or electronic chart plotter

Index